Magical Mix-Ups

Birthdays
and
Bridesmaids

Look out
for other
**Magical
Mix-Ups!**

Magical Mix-Ups
Friends and Fashion

Magical Mix-Ups: Birthdays and Bridesmaids
Published in the UK in 2012 by Nosy Crow Ltd
The Crow's Nest, 10a Lant Street
London SE1 1QR

www. nosycrow.com

Nosy Crow and associated logos are trademarks and/or registered trademarks of Nosy Crow Ltd

Text copyright © Marnie Edwards 2012
Illustrations copyright © Leigh Hodgkinson 2012

The right of Marnie Edwards to be identified as the author
and Leigh Hodgkinson to be identified as the illustrator of this work has been asserted.

A CIP catalogue record for this book is available from the British Library

ISBN: 978 0 85763 104 6

Printed in China

1 3 5 7 9 8 6 4 2

Magical Mix-Ups

Birthdays and Bridesmaids

Marnie Edwards * Leigh Hodgkinson

nosy crow

Who's who in MIXTOPIA

Emerald the Witch

Princess Sapphire

Boris – Emerald's toad

Who's who in FAIRYLAND

King
Tootsie

Queen
Mimsy

Twinkle

Prince
Peasebottom

Princess
Sneezebelle

You'll need these . . .

Drawing
- - - - -
T O O L S

Using different tools helps
create great drawings

PENCIL

COLOURED PENCIL

CRAYON

GLitter at the READY

GET SET
- - -

GO!

Chapter 1

WELCOME
to
Mixtopia!

Mixtopia is a magical land where you should expect the unexpected. A scruffy little witch called Emerald lives there with her trusty toad, Boris, and they think it's the best place in the world . . .

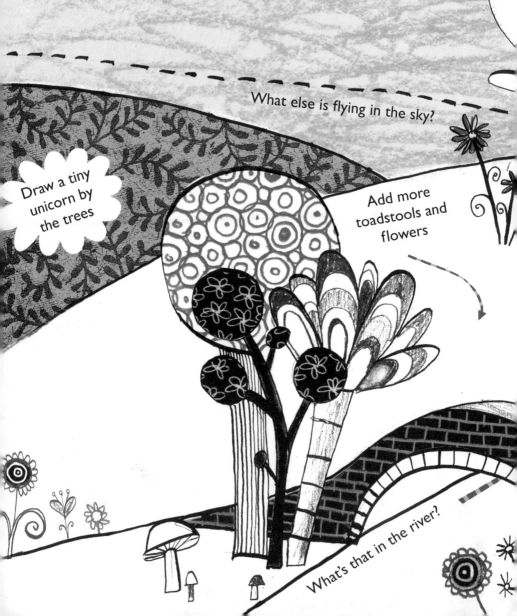

What else is flying in the sky?

Draw a tiny unicorn by the trees

Add more toadstools and flowers

What's that in the river?

Design your
own patterns
on the trees

Add a royal flag

More turrets please!

Draw your own fountain

Flying overhead, Emerald spies the Royal Castle, where her best friend, Princess Sapphire, lives. Next door is a small cottage. Emerald sighs happily. "Home, sweet home!"

Putting her broomstick away neatly in the shed,
Emerald gives her cauldron a stir.
"Hmm, needs more eye of newt, I think,"
she says, popping one in.

Is Emerald's
house messy
or tidy?

Add more
ingredients
to the
cauldron

A vile smell comes from the concoction but
Emerald doesn't mind. Suddenly, she notices
a big, fat envelope propped up on the table . . .

What jars are on the shelves?

What's on
the labels?

Draw a fancy stamp

Draw
Boris's
long, curly
tongue

EMERALD

Emerald opens the envelope and her
hair sparks with surprise. Inside
is a very posh invitation.
"Quick Boris, let's show
Sapphire," says Emerald.

Draw lots
of warts
on Boris

Decorate the
invitation

Dear Emerald the Witch

King Tootsie and Queen Mimsy
of Fairyland
would love you to come to the
wedding of their daughter:

Princess Sneezebelle
to
Prince Peasebottom

Wednesday at 2pm
Do come, do!

And bring your dancing shoes!

1st choice

2nd choice

3rd choice

Dress code:

SPARKLY

Dinner and dancing
afterwards at the

FAIRY DISCO

Carriages at

MIDNIGHT

Wedding list at

Wings'n'wands

RSVP

What
present
would you
give a fairy?

Emerald and Boris crash through Princess Sapphire's open bedroom window.

What can you you see in the mirror?

What else is on the dressing table?

What colour is Sapphire's nail varnish?

Is the rug patterned or plain?

"Now look what you've done, Em!" cries Sapphire, jumping out of her lovely skin. "I've smudged a bit."

More sound effects please!

CRASH!

"Never mind that,"
says Emerald. "Look!"
"Snap!" cries Sapphire. "I'm so excited.
I just can't decide what to wear . . ."

What face is Boris pulling?

Fill in the envelopes

Are there lots of toys on the bed?

Look at all the clothes on the floor!

Add to the tiara tree

Emerald looks at Sapphire's messy bedroom. "Your mum's going to kill you," she says.

What has Boris got on his head?

Add even more stuff to the floor

What books does Sapphire read?

Chapter 2

what NOT to Wear

What else is in the wardrobe?

Princess Sapphire is trying on dresses. "What do you think, Em?" she asks.

What is Sapphire wearing?

Decorate the dresses with pretty patterns

"Should I have my hair up or down?"
asks Sapphire.

Give Sapphire a
lovely hairstyle
and a tiara

Is Emerald
looking bored
or fascinated?

Accessorise
Sapphire with
rings, bracelets
and a necklace

"Shoes!" Sapphire turns to look at her vast collection. "Which go best?"

Design your own shoes

Add the missing shoe to each pair

What is Boris dreaming about?

Draw a heart around the shoes you think Sapphire should wear.

What sort of shoes would Boris wear?

Add some snorey ZZZZeds

"Oh, wake up, Em!" cries Sapphire, catching her friend snoozing. "What are **you** going to wear, anyway? Not that old thing.

Or anything black.

I know . . ."

What does Boris think of Emerald's new look?

Mad hair here, please

Add more patterns to the dress

Add crazy tights here

Don't forget Emerald's party shoes!

Soon Emerald has had enough. With a wave of her wand, she magics up some outfits she likes. Princess Sapphire looks on in approval.

What does her witchy outfit look like? Is it right for the royal wedding?

Add some magic wand zaps and stars

What sort of broomstick should she take?

"Our carriage leaves first thing tomorrow,"
Sapphire tells her friend. "And just one thing:
that horrible toad stays
at home!"

Draw some
wafty whiff
lines around
Boris

Add a swirly
pattern to
Boris's dress

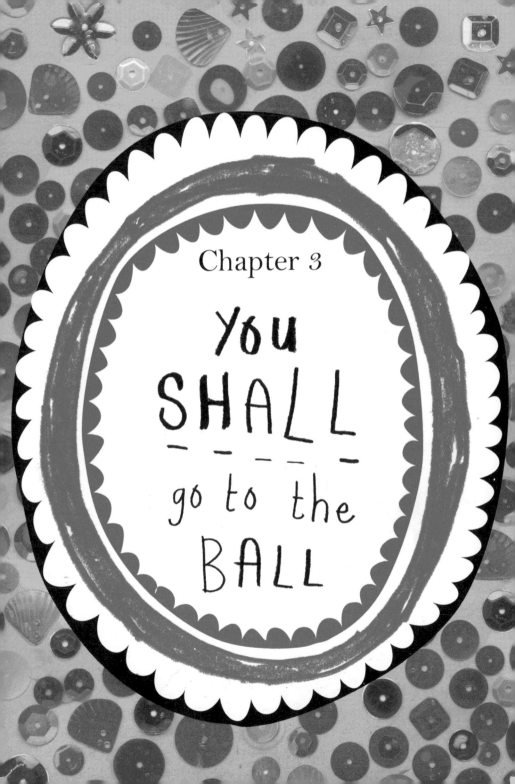

Chapter 3

You
SHALL
- - - -
go to the
BALL

The two girls set off for Fairyland in a beautiful unicorn-drawn carriage.

What is flying in the sky?

How much luggage does Sapphire need?

Where is the wheel?

Oops! Who's lost a suitcase? What's inside?

Princess Sapphire's many bags are strapped to its
roof, and a footman is holding her hatboxes . . .
and the carriage reins!

Add the reins
and more tiny
unicorns

The carriage goes over a bump and Princess Sapphire yelps, rubbing her royal bottom.
"Oh! It's worse than that time I slept on a pea! I'll be black and blue — hey . . . !"

What a lovely view

What's in this pocket?

She points an accusing finger at Emerald's cloak.
"Something moved . . ."

It's Boris!

"I couldn't leave him; he'd have been so lonely, Sapphy," explains Emerald.

Draw dribble on Boris

What's in the hamper?

Put some Boris treats here

"Just make sure he doesn't eat a fairy, then," mutters her friend, darkly.

Boris tries not to dribble.

What is Sapphire about to eat?

Finish this pillar

Draw in the Magic Gates

Just then, they hear the tinkling of bells. As they go through the tiny Magic Gates into Fairyland, they feel themselves shrinking. "We're fairy-sized!" cries Sapphire.

Fill in their passport details

BUTTERFLY ISLAND
15 APRIL 2010

29 JANUARY WITCH WORLD 2011

Name:

Address:

Age:

Occupation:

Add more travel stamps

Name:

Address:

Age:

Occupation:

MERMAIDIA
25TH OCTOBER 2009

Who's standing guard?

What do Sapphire and Emerald's passport photos look like?

The now-tiny carriage sweeps up the
drive to the amazing Fairy Palace.

They've arrived!

buzz buzz

Decorate
the wings
and add more
butterflies

Finish decorating the Palace

Add spots

Draw more flowers

A lovely fairy flutters down
the steps to greet them.

Add wings
to the fairy
footmen

What is this fairy
footman carrying?

"Darlings!"
cries Queen Mimsy.
"You're just in time
for tea!"

Chapter 4

The BAD FAIRY

Just as Emerald is reaching for her fifth cucumber sandwich, the door to the Throne Room crashes open.

Princess Sneezebelle rushes in, holding a velvet ring box and waving a piece of paper around.

"The Fairy Rings!
They've been stolen!" she cries loudly.

The paper falls to the floor.
The thief has left a note!

HA HA HA HAHA!

NO rings means

NO wedding!

SERVES YOU

RIGHT for spoiling

EVERYTHING!

signed

The note's from Twinkle. Write her name here

Princess Sneezebelle sniffs and holds out
the ring box. "Look what she left instead!"
Two Squirt Rings nestle against the soft velvet.
"Who's Twinkle?" asks Emerald.
  "She's Sneezebelle's little cousin,"
    explains Queen Mimsy.

"We have to find her and get the rings back, or the wedding is off!"

At this, Princess Sneezebelle faints delicately on to the chaise longue.

Emerald and Sapphire go to their room to unpack.
Downstairs, all is fairy chaos.

"Why don't we try to find Twinkle?" says Emerald.
"Maybe the Squirt Rings are a clue?"

Add some flowers

Draw a lampshade

Where is Boris?

What's on the floor?

They decide to go to the Fairy High Street to see if they can find a shop that sells Squirt Rings.

Someone might remember Twinkle!

WANDS 'R' US

Finish the shop fronts

What's flying by?

Who's in the windows?

TOADSTOOLZ

Add some fairy dogs

A shop called 'Parties for Smarties' has a sale on:
'Buy 2 Squirt Rings, get a Wiggle Snake free!'

"Look!" cries Princess Sapphire, pointing.
"I bet that's where Twinkle got
her rings."

ONLY
2
SCHOOL
FAIRIES
ALLOWED
IN SHOP AT
ONE TIME

Who
else is going
shopping?

Chapter 5

HOT
on the
TRAIL!

WIGGLE WORMS

MAGIC BUBBLE WANDS

Add funny wigs here

Fill up the boxes

GLITTER PENS

GLOW IN THE DARK BOUNCY BALLS

MONSTE PENCIL TOPPERS

The Party Fairy is very helpful.
"Twinkle was here yesterday," he explains. "Said she'd been saving up all her pocket money, and then spent the lot on party bags and helium balloons. Then she went off to the cake shop!"

Fill up all the shelves in the shop

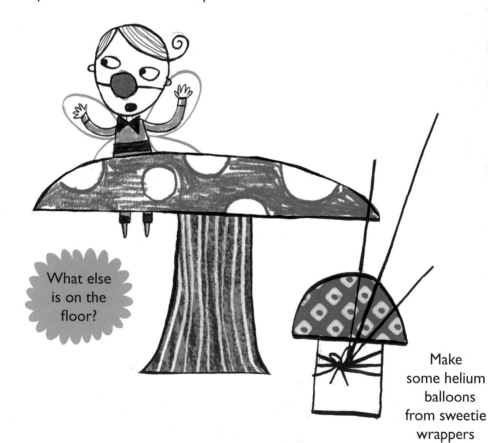

What else is on the floor?

Make some helium balloons from sweetie wrappers

The two girls thank the Party Fairy and head for the cake shop. "Hmmm," says Sapphire. "Squirt Rings, party bags and balloons – what could it all mean?" "Maybe there'll be more clues at the cake shop?" suggests Emerald.

Draw the schoolgirl fairies queuing at the door

What's Boris looking at through his magnifying glass?

What notes has Boris made?

Finish Boris's dotted line

The cake shop is heavenly. There are tiny little cupcakes and enormous chocolate cakes. The meringues look light and fluffy, and as for the cream puffs . . . !

Finish these fairy cakes

Draw a delicious cake in here

The Fairy Baker is putting the finishing touches to an enormous wedding cake, and looks a bit frazzled. "Can I help you?" she asks.

The friends ask about Twinkle
and the fairy points at a large cake box on
the counter. "She'll be here in a minute,"
she says. "Got to pick up her cakes."

What do the cakes spell?

Inside the box are twenty beautiful little fairy cakes,
all decorated with sprinkles and glitter, and letters . . .

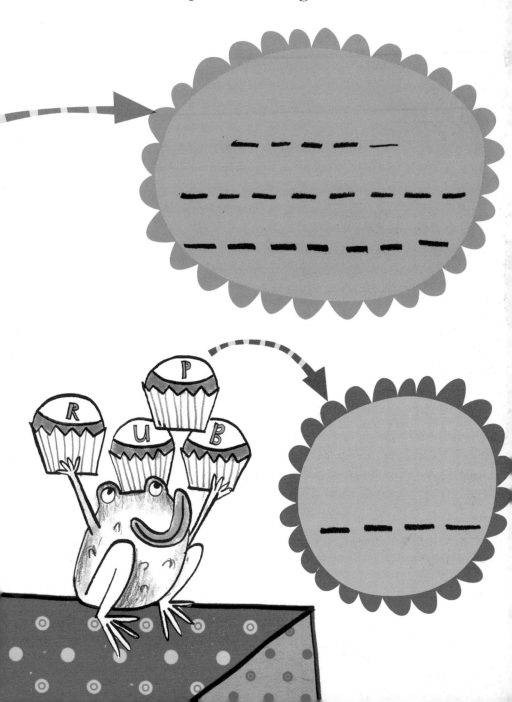

Fairy Bakery Menu

Design your own wallpaper for the bakery walls

Emerald and Sapphire sit down to wait for Twinkle. They order hot chocolate and dainty iced-buns, and Sapphire puts on a pair of huge sunglasses. "I'm in disguise!" she says.
Emerald sighs and takes off her hat. "I can't help thinking those cakes were a clue . . ."

Suddenly, the shop doorbell tinkles and makes them all jump. Boris falls off Emerald's head into a jar of whipped cream.

Who is coming through the door?

What has the Fairy Baker dropped?

Add more splashes

Decorate the label

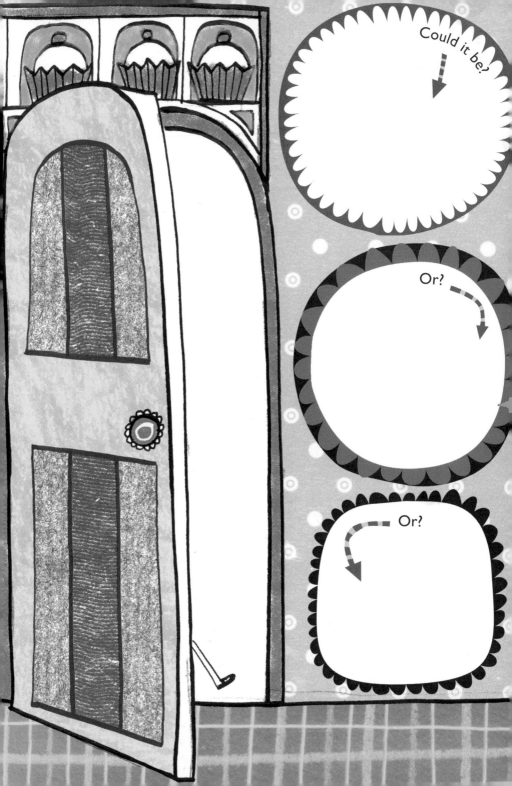

It's Twinkle!
And look what she's wearing round her neck!

Draw a big gloom cloud over Twinkle

Add a check pattern to the floor

Chapter 6

WEDDING

Belles

Finish designing the sunshade

Fairy Bakery

Twinkle puts her box of cakes in her bike basket. "Excuse me," says Sapphire, "but are those the Royal Wedding Rings?"

Attach Twinkle's helium balloons to her bike handle

Add Twinkle's cakes and party bits

"It's my birthday tomorrow, but everyone's forgotten because of the PESKY Royal Wedding!" sobs Twinkle. "I thought if I took the rings, it would stop the wedding and everyone would come to my party instead. I'm really sorry . . ."

Add a pile of birthday presents

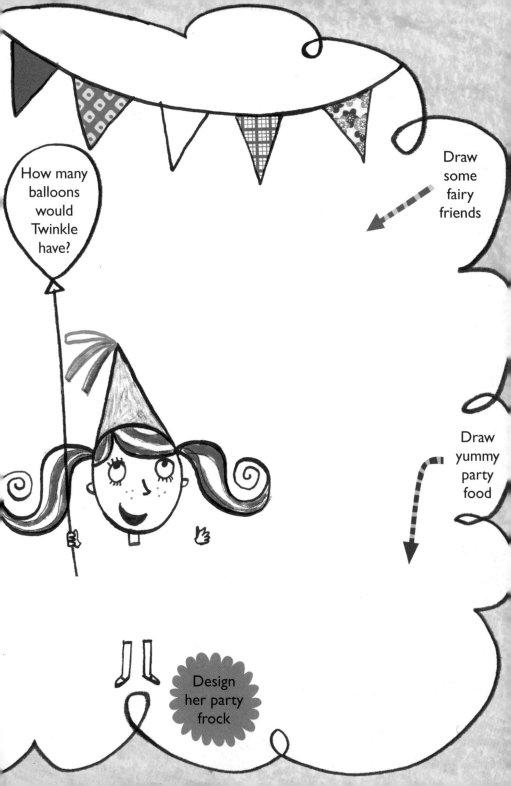

"Let's go and talk to the Queen," says Emerald, waving her wand. They arrive at the Palace in a puff of smoke, causing some fairy alarm. But Twinkle is soon forgiven.

Finish the magic wand swirl

Add more stars

Then Queen Mimsy has a great idea.
"Let's have a magical mix-up – a fantastic
wedding and birthday party in one!"

Finish the fairy faces

Draw an idea light bulb above Queen Mimsy

"I can't wait to see Princess Sneezebelle's dress!" exclaims Sapphire the next day, as she waits impatiently for the bride to arrive at the Fairy Bower.

"And Twinkle's!" says Emerald.
"Here they come!"

Add a perfect rainbow here

Where is Boris?

Add smart hats to the fairy guests

Draw in the Elf King

Draw some magic creatures here

After the ceremony, they all go back to the Palace for a right royal wedding-birthday feast!

What feast food is on the table?

Look at the boy fairies causing mischief

Add more love hearts

Boris is the wedding photographer. Give him a camera

Finish the wedding cake decorations

Finish the tablecloth pattern

As night falls and the stars come out, the Fairy Disco starts. Soon Fairyland is really rocking!

Give the Fairy DJ headphones

Who is this crazy dancer?

After the celebrations, Emerald and Sapphire travel back to Mixtopia. "What a fantastic wedding-birthday!" sighs Sapphire.

Decorate their party bags

What's in Sapphire's party bag?

Emerald agrees. "And Twinkle's are
the best party bags – ever!"

What great
photos Boris
took!

The Big Picture
Draw your favourite moments from the book, and stick in your favourite things

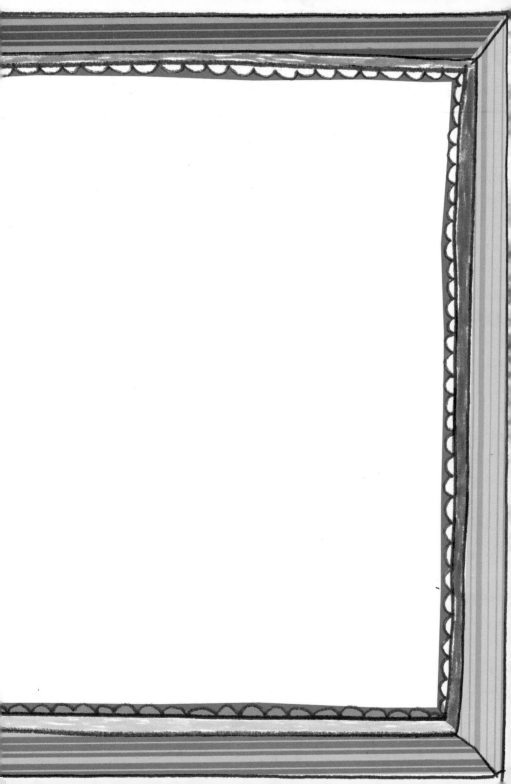

picture
GLOSSARY

If you need a helping hand thinking of things to draw then check these ideas out!

cuddly toys

schoolgirl fairy

Boris's treats

FLY JAM

SNAIL JUICE

stars

dresses

party food

tiaras

fairy pet dogs

fairy friends

musical instruments

wigs

Elf King

camera

moon

(small) (large)

frothy hot
chocolate

cheeky little boy fairies

smart hats

flowers

tea sets

presents